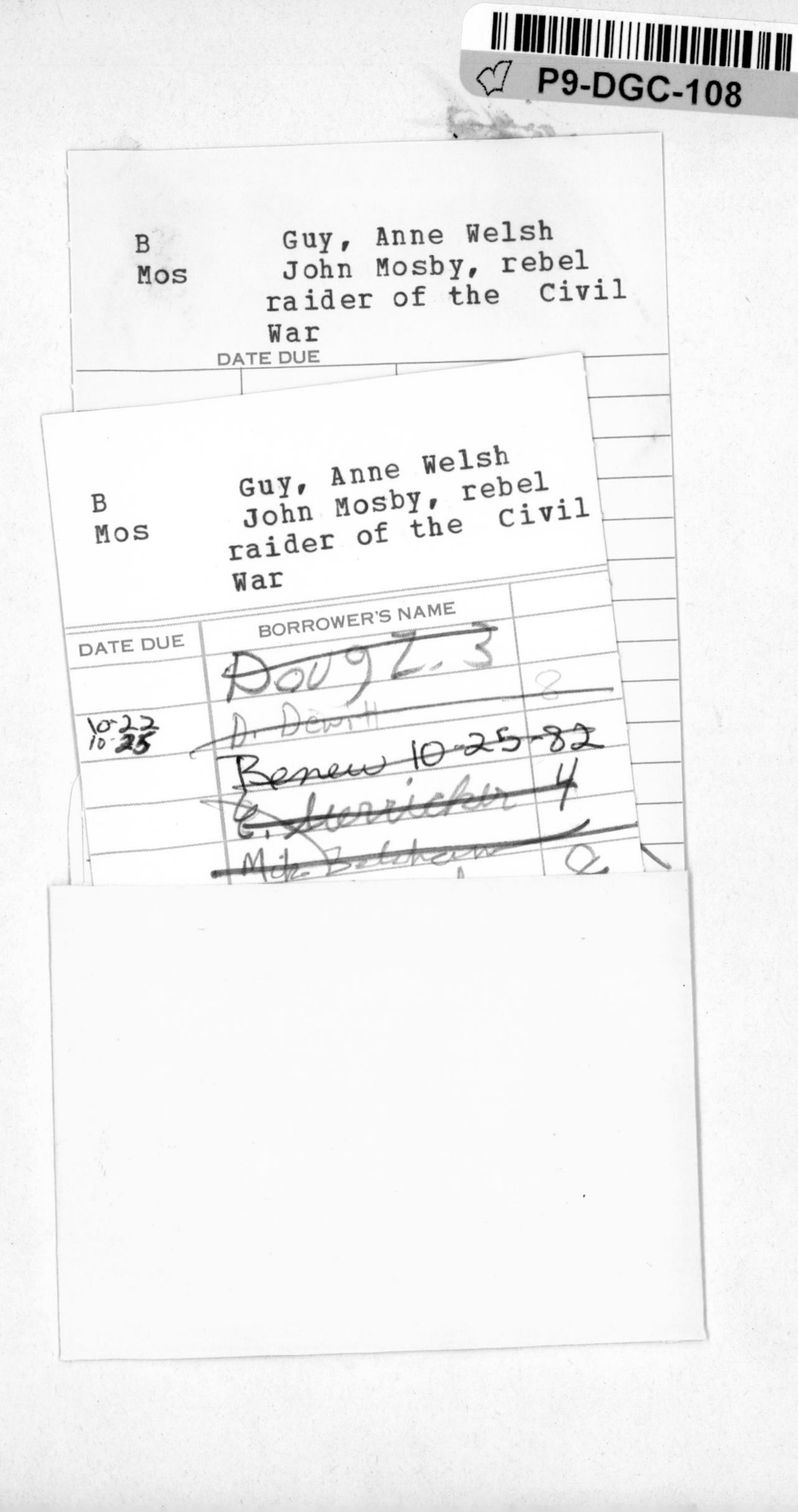
P9-DGC-108
B
Mos
Guy, Anne Welsh
John Mosby, rebel raider of the Civil War
DATE DUE
B
Mos
Guy, Anne Welsh
John Mosby, rebel raider of the Civil War
DATE DUE
BORROWER'S NAME
10-22
10-25
Renew 10-25-82

JOHN MOSBY

Rebel Raider of the Civil War

BY ANNE WELSH GUY

Illustrated with photographs and etchings and with drawings by Richard Guy

ABELARD-SCHUMAN

London New York Toronto

To the three Guy children,

Marianne Frances
Stephen Richard
Clayton Bruce

Library of Congress Catalogue Card Number: 65-12664

LONDON
Abelard-Schuman
Limited
8 King St. WC2

NEW YORK
Abelard-Schuman
Limited
6 West 57th St.

TORONTO
Abelard-Schuman
Canada Limited
896 Queen St. W.

Printed in the United States of America

ACKNOWLEDGMENTS

For the events and background of John Singleton Mosby's life, the author has drawn from the biographical sources in the Library of Congress, Washington, D. C.

The tireless efforts of Mr. Carl Stange of the Prints and Photograph Division of the Library of Congress enabled me to procure reproductions and pictorial matter from the vast collections of that organization. To Mr. John Gott, native of Marshall, Virginia, and great grandson of Mr. Ludwig Lake, I am indebted for the use of photographs from his own private collection. The skill and co-operation of my son, Mr. Richard Guy, commercial artist of Westport, Connecticut, produced the drawings for the earlier chapters for which no photographs were available. The Map of Mosby's Confederacy was contributed by Mr. Paul Stenger of Vienna, Virginia (member of the Fairfax County Centennial Commission).

I also wish to acknowledge the assistance of the following individuals:

Mr. Richard Hurley, Library Supervisor, Fairfax County Schools; Mr. John Gott and Mrs. Hazel Wilson, who read the book in manuscript form and checked it for historical accuracy. Mrs. Esther Douty's Writer's Workshop at George Washington University furnished the original inspiration.

Librarians Edith Brock, Ruth Enlow Library, Oakland, Maryland; Jeanette Murray, Ocean City, Maryland, Library; and Dorothy Moore, Worcester County Library, Snow Hill, Maryland, gave me research assistance.

For secretarial help, I wish to thank my typists, Mrs. Ira Shimasaki and Mrs. James Canty.

Contents

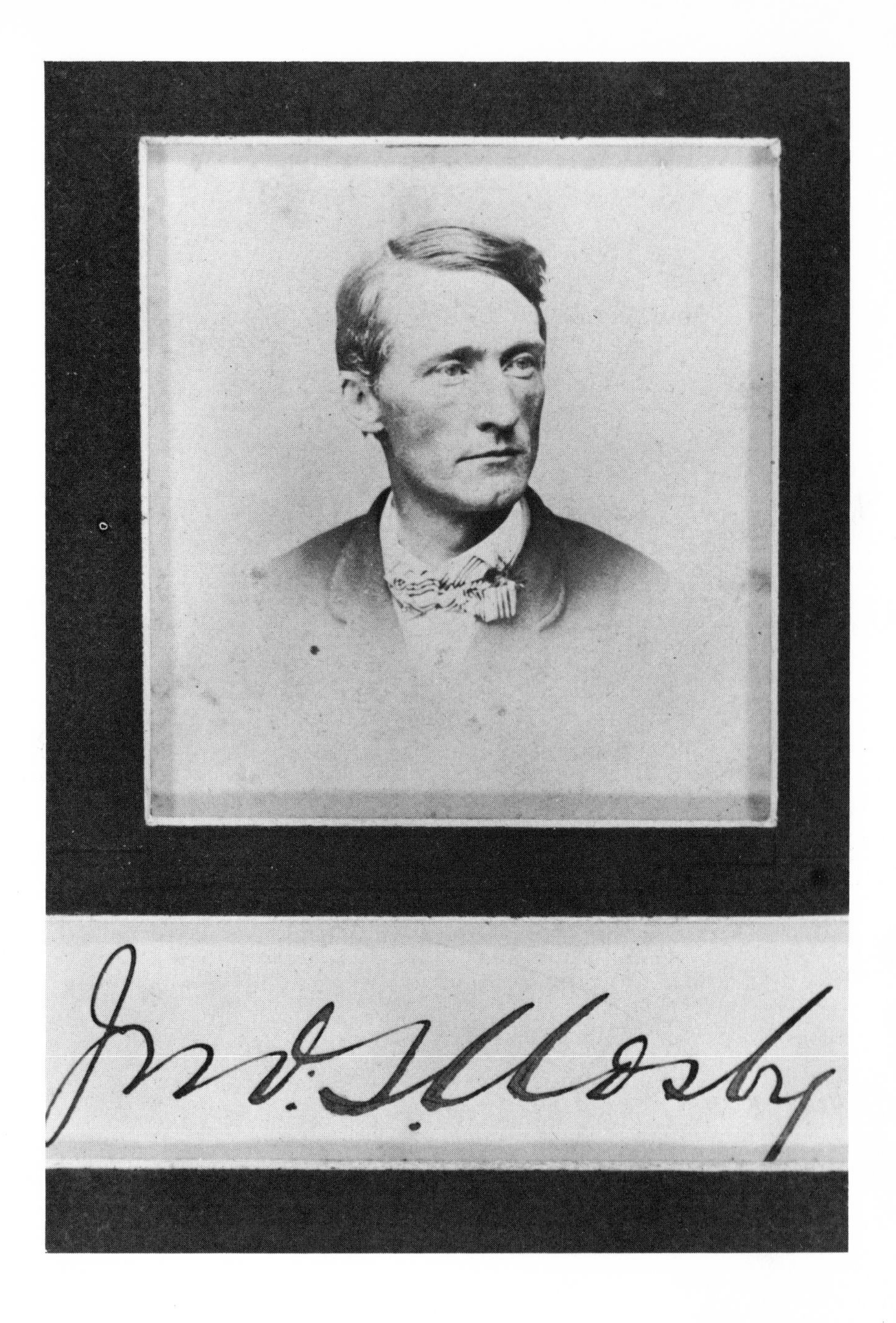
Jno. S. Mosby

Historical Note

THE fiercest, most tragic war ever fought by the United States lasted four years — from 1861 to 1865. It was called the Civil War, meaning war inside one nation.

On March 4, 1861, when Abraham Lincoln became president, the people were divided. The ugly question of slavery had split the Union. North and South did not agree, and each side thought it was right.

The North believed that nothing was so important as the Union and that it must be saved, no matter what the sacrifice. The South believed in the right of each state to decide for itself about such questions as slavery, and that each state had the right to leave the Union if it desired to do so. The quarrel became so bitter that the nation broke apart. The South set up a new government at Richmond, Virginia, adopted a new flag, and named itself the Confederate States of America. The commanding officer of the army defending Richmond was Robert E. Lee, one of the greatest generals in American history.

American fought against American — the brave "Johnny Reb," as the Confederate soldier in his gray uniform was called, against the courageous "Yank" in Union blue. The war was finally won by the North, and Lee surrendered at Appomattox Court House on April 9, 1865, to the great Union general, Ulysses S. Grant.

One of the most feared officers in this bloody struggle was Colonel John Singleton Mosby, Confederate commander of the 43rd Virginia Battalion of the Cavalry. Beloved and revered by the South, it is only in the hundred years that have passed since the war that he has become recognized by the North as one of the great Confederates. Called "guerilla" and "horse thief" by the northern armies, he kept their troops frantic with rage over his activities.

Mosby and his band were raiders. They operated around Washington and in northern Virginia, an area which became known as Mosby's Confederacy. The plan of their raids was always the same; strike, then disappear into the hills and woods. They captured guns and supplies, men and horses; they burned storehouses, derailed trains, destroyed camps and bridges. By tieing up thousands of Federal troops in the rear, Mosby is thought to have delayed the defeat of the southern armies by as much as a year.

General Robert E. Lee, complimented him in dispatches more often than any other Confederate officer. On January 28, 1915, one year before his death, Mosby's college, the University of Virginia, put this on a bronze medal:

> "Endowed with the gift of friendship which won for you the confidence of both Lee and Grant, you have proven yourself a man of war, a man of letters, and a man of affairs, worthy of the best traditions of your university and state, to both of whom you have been a loyal son."

★ 1 ★

First School

A CURL of smoke rose from the tall chimneys of a big brick house which sat, snug and comfortable, among oak trees and pines on a farm near Charlottesville, Virginia. It was a bright September morning in the year 1839.

Suddenly the door of the house opened, and a small, sandy-haired boy, lunch basket in hand, came bursting out. He ran across the wide front porch and down the steps to the driveway. Then he glared up at the woman and the tall Negro boy who had followed him.

"I'm not going to have Aaron walk to school with me, Mother." "I want to go alone. By myself. I know the way. I'm not afraid."

The boy's blue eyes were blazing. His mouth was set in a stubborn line.

Quickly the woman ran down the steps and put her hands on the boy's shoulders. The Negro followed more slowly, his white teeth flashing in a smile as he looked from the small boy to the woman.

"Now, John," she said gently, "the school is two miles away. That is a long way for a boy not yet seven years old to walk alone. Remember, your father killed a bear in these woods last week. You know you want to start school. You love to hear the stories that your father and I read to you. But you must learn to read them yourself, and to do sums, and to play with other boys your own age.

"I can't let you go alone. I would worry all day long. Aaron will go with you in the mornings and he will come home with you in the afternoons. Come now, run along. And mind that you stay close to Aaron."

Without another word, John squirmed out of his mother's hands and ran down the driveway, through a gate, and on into a narrow crooked pathway that led off into the woods. Aaron ran after him. After a while the small boy stopped running and the two of them settled down to a pleasant hike among the sweet-smelling, tall pines.

"I'm going to be a hunter like my father," remarked the boy presently. "As soon as I am twelve, my father has promised me a gun. I shall go hunting every Satur-

day and bring back deer and rabbit and bear. I shall always go alone. I shall have a big drink of hot coffee before I leave, just as my father does, and I shall be the best hunter in the whole state of Virginia."

Aaron looked down at the frail, thin little fellow beside him and his white teeth flashed again. But he said nothing.

They walked along in silence for a while. The air was crisp. The pine needles had a sharp sweetness.

"Have you ever heard of Robin Hood, Aaron?" asked John.

The Negro boy shook his head.

"He lived in a wood like this, only in England. My father read me a story about him. He had a band of merry men and they lived deep in the forest. He helped those who were in trouble. And he had a horn to blow when he needed his merry men to come to his aid. Perhaps I shall go away from home and live in a forest when I am a man and be like Robin Hood."

The two boys came at last to the little schoolhouse. The schoolmaster stood at the door, ringing a small hand bell. Boys were hurrying into the schoolhouse, laughing and shoving as they ran. Aaron turned to leave, but John was suddenly shy.

"Why don't you stay all day today, Aaron?" he suggested. "Then you won't have to walk that long way by yourself."

When the Negro boy shook his head, John patted his lunch box slyly.

"Just till noon anyway," he begged. "There's fried chicken in here — lots of it — enough for me and you both."

The Negro's eyes rolled hungrily. He strolled over to a tree and stretched out on the ground as John ran quickly into the schoolhouse.

John was one of the last ones out at noon. The morning had been a new and exciting adventure for him. The schoolmaster taught spelling and ciphering. He had praised John for being quick to understand and learn. John's cheeks were flushed with happiness as he ran out into the sunny schoolyard to eat his lunch. But the sight that met his eyes turned him pale.

On the stump of a tree stood Aaron, his eyes bulging with fright. Around him clustered the big boys of the school, shouting and laughing.

"How much am I bid, fellows?" shouted the biggest boy, who was holding Aaron by the arm. "Come on. Bid 'em up. He goes to the highest bidder."

"I'll give my apple for him," shouted a boy, laughing loudly.

"A piece of pumpkin pie," shouted another. "He's not worth more than a piece of pie."

"Sure he is," cried a third. "Let's see his muscles. I'm willing to give my whole lunch for him."

GUY

The auctioneer lifted the Negro's arm and pushed back his sleeve.

"Show your muscles," he ordered. Then turning to the boys, he called out, "Do I hear any more bids? Sold for a box of lunch! Going—going—"

A scream interrupted him. "Let go of my friend," shouted a shrill voice. A small dynamo suddenly exploded in the auctioneer's face. A lunch basket hit the auctioneer, and two small fists began pummelling him.

"Hey, you!" cried the big boy. He let go of Aaron, who quickly headed for the woods. He grabbed John by the wrists. "Hey, quit that. Say, who is this little punk anyway? I can't get loose of him."

John, screaming and sobbing, slapped with all his might at the head and stomach of the larger boy.

At last the boy untangled John's wiry little arms and set him down on the ground.

"Say, can't you take a joke?" he demanded. "It was only a game we were playing."

John, noticing that Aaron had disappeared, mopped the tears off his face with the back of his fists. He stopped to pick up his scattered lunch.

"Whew, is that little fellow going to be a *fighter,*" said the big boy to the others as they walked off. He rubbed his scratched face.

Aaron walked home with John that afternoon but he never came to school again.

It was the last time that John Singleton Mosby had a bodyguard.

"John doesn't need protection," his father said. "He has courage. He tackled a boy older and stronger than himself to protect Aaron. He's stronger than he looks."

Still his mother could not stop worrying over him.

"Perhaps we should think about sending John to the Widow Frye's school," she suggested to his father. "The Widow Frye is opening a school right at the edge of our farm. Even if it is run by a woman, it would be much closer. It is a school for both boys and girls, and his sisters could go too. Perhaps the boys there would not be so rough." She sighed.

"John is such a delicate boy. I'm afraid he will never live to become a man."

★ 2 ★

"Bookworm"

AFTER two months at the country school, John Mosby started to the Widow Frye's school adjoining their farm. It was just a rude log hut in the woods, with a spring bubbling past, from which the children drank deep, cool water out of a gourd hanging from a tree.

Widow Frye taught her pupils writing, ciphering and reading. John learned very fast. He especially liked to read, and pored over the Peter Parley books, which were the school readers of that time. The pictures were very exciting to him — many were of soldiers of the Revolution dying on the field of battle or galloping into action. Fighting! Going to war! Being a soldier! It must be the greatest, bravest thing any boy could do.

Each day, as soon as he had finished the hour of ciphering — which he disliked — and the hour of writ-

ing in copybooks, copying the round clear letters over and over until the script flowed perfectly across the page, John would pull a book from under his slate and lose himself in a story. He read so constantly that he often ran out of books. Then he would read his favorite chapters over and over. One day his teacher brought him the story of Marion the Swamp Fox, the brave soldier of the Revolution who hid in the swamps of South Carolina and outwitted the British in many narrow escapes and adventures. On and on he read, now and then exclaiming aloud with delight over the story.

Playtime came and the children swarmed joyously out into the snow. There was a fine hill by the school, and in winter coasting was one of the sports the children loved.

"Come on out and coast, John," shouted Henry, the Widow Frye's son, as he pulled on his coat and mittens. But John was too absorbed in his story even to hear. Henry was John's seatmate. The boys sat, two to a bench, side by side. Henry was the same age as John, although he was a much larger boy. He could not read very well but he was good at games. He was scornful of the "bookworm" who was constantly winning praise from Henry's mother, the Widow, and who could seldom be coaxed to join in playing marbles, tops, catch, racing or any of the outdoor games that Henry liked.

"No wonder he's so skinny and small," Henry told the other boys. "He can't do anything but read."

That afternoon as John and his two sisters stepped out of the schoolhouse door, a snowball hit him squarely in the shoulder, the soft snow bursting and spattering all over him and his younger sister who stood on the step beside him. Victoria began to sob.

"Here comes the sissy," shouted Henry gleefully, peeping over a snow fort as he packed another snowball. "Sissy, fraidy cat, teacher's pet!"

"Give it to him good," shouted another boy, and the second snowball hit John full in the chest.

John's blue eyes blazed. Rushing forward, he gave one leap over the fort and flung himself with such force on the surprised boy that he knocked him flat to the ground. The two boys tangled there in the snow, rolling over and over, feet and fists flying. The others watched in amazement. Suddenly the schoolhouse door was flung open and an angry voice called.

"Henry! John! Stop that fighting! Come here at once!" Reluctantly the two boys scrambled to their feet, brushed the snow off and walked back into the school.

Sending Elizabeth and the still sobbing Victoria on home alone, the teacher closed the door and faced the culprits.

"I guess it was really my fault," began Henry.

But Widow Frye cut him short. "You were both fighting. No excuses or apologies. Walk over to your desk, turn your backs and bend over."

Taking a stout switch from several that stood in the corner, she gave each boy five sharp lashes.

"You know I don't allow fighting," she repeated sternly. "Let's have no more of it."

As the two boys walked away, to Henry's surprise, John turned and winked at him, his blue eyes twinkling. Henry looked at John with a new respect. Yes, there was something about the "bookworm" that Henry was beginning to like.

★ 3 ★

In Self-Defense

AFTER several years at Widow Frye's school, John was ready for the Academy. The Academy was in Charlottesville. It prepared the children for high school and for college. John was only ten years old, but he had his own horse. He loved cantering to school in the early morning hours, and back again in the late afternoon. It gave him time to think and to be alone; to listen to the chatter of squirrels, and to enjoy the woods that he loved.

Sometimes it was dark by the time he got home. He would stop and gaze across the valley at the yellow glow coming from the windows of Monticello. It was the home that Thomas Jefferson, third President of the United States and author of the Declaration of Inde-

pendence, had built on a knoll as a mountain retreat. John remembered some of the stirring words of the Declaration. He would say them out loud to himself.

"We hold these truths to be self-evident, that all men are created equal. . . .And for the support of this Declaration . . .we mutually pledge to each other our Lives, our Fortunes, and our Sacred Honor." These words made him feel brave and strong. They made him think!

Only twenty-five boys went to the Academy. They studied Greek and Latin and algebra under two headmasters. The headmasters were very strict, and John spent long hours studying. He asked little help from anyone. He liked Greek and Latin but hated mathematics. A frail, delicate-looking boy still, with keen blue eyes, he talked little unless a discussion came up which interested him. Then he would talk with great earnestness to anyone who would listen.

During the time that John attended the Academy, his sisters were tutored at home by a governess, Miss Abby Southwick, who came from Massachusetts. She was bitterly opposed to the owning of slaves. She and John became great friends and John listened thoughtfully to all she said. He wondered why it was so bad to be a slave. He was very fond of the slaves his father owned. They were well cared for and seemed happy.

But Miss Southwick said, "End slavery or the Union

will end." John thought hard about her words and about slavery and the Union.

When John was sixteen, he was ready to enter the University of Virginia. The University was not as much of a thrill to him as the Academy at Charlottesville had been. The only difference was that he lived at a boardinghouse in town instead of riding home each day. Here again his favorite subjects and the ones in which he made the best marks were Greek and Latin. He especially liked poetry. He found his studies easy and, for the first time in his school life, he began to take the time to enjoy the companionship of other boys in his classes. He entered into the social life of the college and then, in his second year, something tragic happened.

A big blustering bully of a fellow – a classmate named Turpin – fought continually with all the boys. He had been known to pick up a rock as a weapon or draw a knife if his temper was high. He was one to avoid.

One day, following a discussion he had had with John, Turpin sent him a message. He was coming to "eat him blood raw on sight." The "bookworm" received the news without comment. However, he dropped a small pistol into his pocket before he started off for math class.

At noon, Turpin came to John's boardinghouse. He shouted to John to come out on the porch. John came out, calling to Turpin as he came. But instead of answering, Turpin sprang at John. Quick as a flash John drew his gun and fired, giving Turpin a wound in the neck that sent him reeling to the floor unconscious.

John was expelled from school for this unlawful act. He was arrested and at a trial he was found "guilty" and sentenced to spend twelve months in jail. Although he was released in six months because of a pardon by the governor of Virginia, John was heartbroken over the whole affair.

But although John was quick of temper and stubborn, he could never stay angry long or hold a grudge. While in jail, he made friends with the very lawyer who had fought against him and put him there.

"I can see that law is important," he told the lawyer. "It can help a man get out of trouble. I think I should like to become a lawyer." The lawyer brought him law books to read and offered John a place in his office when he left jail.

John studied for three years in the law office after serving out his punishment. He became a lawyer and later opened his own office. He fell in love with Pauline Clark, a dark-eyed girl from Kentucky. Their marriage was a love affair from beginning to end, and they settled down to a peaceful life in the little Virginia town of Bristol. Among their wedding gifts was Aaron, who gladly followed the master of his youth into his new home.

It seemed that John Mosby's fighting days were over, except for the legal fighting that would be done in the courtroom of a small town.

And then came the Civil War.

★ 4 ★

War Clouds Over Virginia

"ATTENTION! Stand to horse!—Prepare to mount! Mount!"

John Mosby swung into his saddle swiftly and easily. The other men, most of them new to horseback, did not do so well.

Captain Grumble Jones roared in anger.

"Come out of the woods, you fools. Get down off of those horses. Try again. Make it smooth and easy. This is the cavalry."

Over and over the men tried. Again and again. Snapping their heels together. Bodies tall and straight. Right hand on the reins. Eyes to the front.

"Straighten those shoulders, Mosby," shouted the captain. He gave John a punch in the stomach.

Grumble Jones was a hard, rough man. He did not

look like the captain of a company of cavalry. He wore blue jeans and a dirty rumpled jacket.

But John Mosby liked him at once. John had just joined the cavalry. He wanted to know all the things that a cavalry man should know, and he knew that Grumble Jones would teach him.

War had come to Virginia and the states of the Union that April of the year 1861.

It was Civil War. Some called it the War Between the States.

Six states had left the Union and when Virginia seceded also, John Mosby closed up his law office at once and enlisted as a private in the cavalry. He had left home that morning to join Grumble Jones's troop.

"It should only take about three months," he told his wife, Pauline, comfortingly, as he got ready to leave for camp. He kissed her and his little son and daughter good-bye. "In three months we should be able to outsmart those Yankees and drive them back north where they belong. Then I will be at home with you again." He cupped his hand under her chin. "I'll have to hurry or the war will be over before I have a chance to become famous," he said, smiling.

Pauline laid her head against his shoulder. She did not want him to see the tears in her dark eyes. "People will be surprised to see you fighting with the South, John," she said. "Everyone thought you were backing the Union and that you felt the states should stick together."

"So I was backing the Union," Mosby answered. "Night after night I have walked the floor, thinking this matter out. Virginia has left the Union. My first loyalty is to Virginia. I must go with her. President Lincoln is sending seventy-five thousand men down to fight the South. I couldn't fight against Virginia. I love her. It would be like fighting against my own mother."

After his drill with Grumble Jones that afternoon, Mosby led his horse to the stables. It was a fine thoroughbred that his father had sent to him. Aaron was there, waiting to take the horse from him. Aaron's white teeth flashed in the usual smile of affection when his master came in. He was happy that the body servants were allowed to come with their masters to clean their boots and saddles and to tend their horses.

A bugle note rang out as Mosby started toward his quarters. He took a deep breath of the sweet spring air.

"I hope I shall be sent into the front lines at once," he thought. "I want to go into the places of greatest danger. I want to get this war over quickly."

Mosby was the smallest and frailest of all the men in the company. At 28, he weighed only 125 pounds and was 5 feet 9 inches tall. He did not look like a soldier any more then Grumble Jones looked like a captain.

That night as he walked his post on guard duty, he

felt very cold and lonely. He thought of the straw pallet upon which he would sleep and longed for his warm bed at home and for his wife and family. He looked up at the twinkling stars and watched them through the night until they began to fade and turn pale in the early light of morning. How often he had risen under those stars for a long day of hunting in his beloved woods, or to take an early canter on his horse before school. His thoughts went to Washington, the capitol, lying under those same stars with the Stars and Stripes floating over it in the gentle morning breeze.

Strange, he thought, sadly, that the Stars and Stripes are the flag of an enemy and that Washington is no longer my capital.

The Halt. It took 18 long days to reach Richmond.

★ 5 ★

First Battle, Picket Duty and a Dream

IT was a day of drizzling rain.

Grumble Jones and his one hundred and two cavalrymen were leaving training camp. They were to join the army at Richmond, the new capital of the seven Confederate States that had left the union.

John Mosby's heart was as dreary as the weather as the men started slowly off down the road. At their head a homemade Confederate flag waved — three broad stripes of red and white, with seven stars sprinkled on a blue field. At the rear rode the body servants who would take care of their masters.

It took eighteen long days to reach Richmond. During those weeks, as the men rode through the many little towns along the way, Mosby felt his spirits begin to lift. People came rushing from houses to wave. Girls threw

Soldiers in bright uniforms marched into Richmond.

flowers and kisses. They liked the way the men sat tall on their horses and curbed them. Old men waved their canes and cheered and hobbled along a little way with the servants. In spite of himself, Mosby began to feel gay and excited. Why, this was almost like a picnic. When some of the boys took out their banjos and began to strum, he kept time with his fingers on his horse's neck and hummed. He was going to enjoy war.

They found a city of tents when they reached Richmond! Soldiers were everywhere. More soldiers than John Mosby had ever seen before. Troops poured from the trains. From Texas, Louisiana, Georgia, companies came swinging down the streets. Soldiers in bright new uniforms were marching on parade. Bugle calls and drum rolls and band music could be heard from all sides. Batteries of artillery and wagons loaded with ammunition rumbled up and down the streets.

Grumble Jones took his men right through the center of all this activity. And as the company rode by, all eyes turned to look, and people cheered.

For a short time Grumble Jones's men trained at Richmond. Then they set out to the Shenandoah Valley to join the First Virginia Cavalry under Colonel J. E. B. (Jeb) Stuart, one of the most daring and dashing officers of the Confederate Army.

Mosby gasped in surprise when he first caught sight of Jeb Stuart. What a huge fellow he was, with his flow-

Col. *J.E.B. (Jeb) Stuart*

ing, curly red beard and mustache. On his hat was a gold star. An ostrich feather drooped at one side. He wore snow-white gloves, and every button on his uniform gleamed. When Mosby looked into Stuart's dancing blue eyes and heard the roar of his hearty laughter, he knew that this was a leader to whom he would give all his loyalty, affection and admiration.

Grumble Jones's company was a crack outfit and Stuart was glad to get it. He put the new company to use immediately as a scout troop, to learn the plans and to watch and report on the movements of the enemy. Mosby was chosen by Grumble to ride at the head of the company. Grumble gave him the most dangerous duties and sent him on the most dangerous missions. Still, these duties did not put him into the front line of actual fighting, and he was impatient.

In July, 1861, at Manassas Junction, on a quiet little creek called Bull Run, John got his first smell of powder. Manassas was the first big battle of the Civil War. John was close enough to the battlefield to hear the mighty roar of cannon and the bursting of shells. He heard for the first time the Rebel yell – a yell so terrifying that it made the hair rise on the back of his neck.

He watched the whooping Confederates dash in from all sides, fighting hand to hand. It was a great victory for the South. After the battle he rode over the field filled with dead and wounded, a feeling of sadness mixed with the exultation in his heart.

That night he wrote to his wife, "The Yankees gave way; they abandoned everything; they fled like a flock of panic-stricken sheep." But he did not tell her how disappointed he was that Grumble Jones's men were held in reserve behind the lines, and that he did not get to fire a single shot from the fine new rifle that lay on his horse's shoulders.

Instead he told her about his slave. "Aaron," he wrote, "considers himself next in command to Captain Jones. He is sure the Yank army are out to capture him."

Aaron called the Cavalry "his boys." He kept fresh horses ready and waiting. He helped to take care of the sick and wounded by "doctoring" them with his famous corn cakes, but when a shell fell too near, he was off into the mountains where he stayed for days.

All during the winter of 1862, Mosby saw little action. The Federals withdrew to Washington. The Virginia cavalry was posted along the Potomac on picket to watch them. Twenty-four hours at a stretch, three times a week, Mosby's company rode on guard.

After a time Mosby grew to like the long lonely nights under the stars in the bramble thickets and bushes and pine woods along the river. It was much more interesting than the routine of camp, which he disliked. There were unexpected, exciting skirmishes with the enemy. They were very close, often in plain sight across the Potomac. And being alone gave John time to think. Marion, the Swamp Fox, had hidden in bramble thickets such as these. The old stories of his younger days came back to him. As he watched the black branches of the trees swaying in the moonlight, a plan began to form in his mind — a dream to take shape. "I have learned every path and cowtrail and road around Washington. If only I had my own command," he thought, "just a small group of men, I would not have to wait for orders. We would attack swiftly — take the enemy by surprise, mystify them."

The wheels of his mind kept turning this plan over and over during the long, cold, late winter. But it was not until March that something happened that helped Mosby in working it out.

In March, Jeb Stuart, who was now a brigadier general, made Mosby his own personal scout.

Union troops

★ 6 ★

A Daring Ride

GENERAL Jeb Stuart always carried field glasses over his shoulder and he was looking through their powerful lenses now, gazing at the troops of George B. McClellan, the Union general.

McClellan's forces were massed within a mile of Jeb Stuart's cavalry. In March, the Union troops had begun to move away from Washington. "On to Richmond" was their slogan. "Capture Richmond and bring the South to her knees."

Jeb Stuart moved his field glasses from one side to the other, sweeping the horizon. Then he turned to an officer who stood beside him.

"I wonder if McClellan's army is really trailing us or just pretending," Stuart said, with a frown on his handsome face.

McClellan's forces were massed within a mile of Jeb Stuart.

Instantly John Mosby, who had been watching Stuart for some time, stepped up and answered quickly.

"Let me go to the rear of McClellan's army for you. I'll find out. Give me a guide and I'll go at once."

Stuart watched Mosby as he walked away. Mosby had not come under his notice until lately. Now he began to interest Stuart greatly. How swiftly Mosby moved, and noiselessly — with the ease and grace of a slender boy — yet how fearless and confident he was.

"A perfect scout," Stuart murmured to the officer. "One who thinks for himself. I shall keep him near me."

By the next morning, after riding all night, Mosby was back from his scouting trip. He swung down from his horse and hurried to Stuart.

"It is only a trick, sir," he reported. "Only a small body of troops are there, with no support. Most of the force has retreated. They are just making a big noise. You can settle them."

Stuart's eyes twinkled and he put his arm around Mosby's shoulders.

"You and Grumble Jones and his men may join me in that pleasure," he said.

By June, a few months later, McClellan moved up again, this time with one hundred thousand men and this time much closer to Richmond.

General Robert E. Lee, one of the greatest soldiers in American history, was in command of the defense of

Richmond. General Lee had only sixty thousand men. He needed to know what the enemy was up to before he made his plans. He called upon Jeb Stuart and once again Jeb Stuart sent for his scout, Mosby.

It took three days and nights of dangerous scouting within enemy lines, but before Mosby returned he had found out all that General Lee wanted to know. Dusty and hot, too tired to stand on his feet, he threw himself down on the grass by Stuart. With his finger he mapped out the position of McClellan's army in the grass.

"McClellan has a strong force," he said. "But there are only a few cavalry pickets protecting his life. Part of the way the road is clear. If you will cross the railroad and cut around *behind* McClellan, you will find nothing — nothing at all — to stop you. You can capture their supplies. You can force the northern army to pull back." Mosby's eyes began to sparkle. "Why, you can ride clear around the enemy and get right between him and his storehouses."

"A mad plan," said Stuart, roaring with laughter. "But I like it. A cavalry raid clear around an enemy. Of course the chances are ten to one against our being able to escape capture! Still, I like the idea. What would I do without you, John?"

Stuart sent the information immediately to General Lee and received permission to make the cavalry raid. Early the next morning, a yellow rose in his buttonhole,

General Stuart's ride around McClellan

he started gaily off with twelve hundred of his Confederate horsemen. At the head rode Mosby, beside his beloved general.

It was a wonderful, clear June day and the spirits of the men were high. Stuart took out his banjo and began to sing. Mosby's voice soon joined in the song RIDING A RAID, written especially for the cavalry.

Come tighten your girth and slacken your reins;
Come buckle your blanket and holster again;
Try the click of your trigger and balance your blade
For he must ride sure that goes Riding a Raid.

Deep into enemy territory they went, completely cut off from any Confederate help. For three days they rode, so steadily that many of the men dropped asleep, exhausted, in their saddles. They went completely around McClellan's army, burning storehouses, wagons and supplies, derailing railroad trains, destroying camps and bridges. They returned to Richmond and General Lee with one hundred and sixty-six prisoners and two hundred and sixty horses and mules, and the stirring news that McClellan had been blocked.

This victory made the Confederate Army and its generals very happy. Both in the North and in the South the name of Mosby began to be heard. General Lee commended him for a promotion to captain.

Stuart said, "You are my eyes and my ears, Mosby.

You shall be my own personal scout for the rest of this war."

But John had a better plan. This was his opportunity to tell Stuart about it.

"Give me my own command," he begged. "Lend me just a handful of men. We have found that the enemy looks always to the front. It lets the rear take care of itself. If I had my own band of men, I could attack the stores of supplies and wagon trains at the rear. I should strike swiftly, surprise the enemy, then go into hiding. I should keep the enemy worried, so worried that thousands of Union men could be kept from fighting at the front."

Stuart listened. "Your plan is a good one," he said.

But he needed Mosby. He needed him in the cavalry. He needed him as his scout. He did not want to let go such a brave man.

For half a year more, Mosby rode with Stuart and scouted for him.

Again and again Mosby brought up his plan for his own little band. Stuart always listened. And at last, late one afternoon, Stuart decided to give Mosby his way.

Map of Mosby's Confederacy

★ 7 ★

The Strange Squad

WITH a jangling of sabers and a clatter of hoofs, Jeb Stuart and the First Virginia Cavalry rode off toward the Confederate Headquarters at Fredericksburg.

Left alone in territory filled with thousands of enemy troops, Mosby and nine troopers, loaned to him by Stuart, sat on their horses and watched them go. It was an afternoon in January, 1863. This was the chance Mosby had waited for — the fulfillment of his dream.

As the sound of hoof beats died away, the men turned to look at their new leader. The late afternoon sun slanted upon him and upon his big gray horse, prancing and pawing impatiently on the highway. Mosby was no longer dressed in the careless, dusty clothes of a scout. His gray uniform was pressed and spotless. On his gray plush hat was a dark plume which waved jauntily. His tall cavalry boots were polished and shining. No saber hung at his side, but two large Colt revolvers were in his belt. When he spoke, his cold blue eyes blazed with pride and eagerness and his glance seemed to pierce into the eyes of the men looking at him.

He spoke briefly.

"This will be our valley, men. We will fight here on the Virginia side of Washington and along the Potomac. Between the Blue Ridge Mountains on the west and the Catoctin Mountains on the east, from Leesburg down to Warrenton, the towns are far apart. The valley is rich with food. Gaps through the mountains will give us quick getaway roads, and caves will give us places to hide.

"This is our plan. We will live within the enemy lines. No camps. No tents or quarters. At night, scatter two by two or alone. Try to find friendly homes in which to sleep. Tell no one who you are. If you can't find homes you can trust, sleep by fences, in graveyards or in haystacks. Hide yourselves in the woods. Wait my secret call to come together at places I shall choose. Always carry pistols.

"Sabers are no better than cornstalks against the fire and shock of a six-shooter.

"Tonight we go toward Fairfax Court House,

which is bursting with Union troops. Only a long chain of pickets — a half mile apart — are guarding the banks of the Potomac and the city of Washington. We'll take secret, unknown paths. We'll leave our horses at a friend's farm. After dark, we'll strike. Follow me."

He raised his hand in a quick gesture and galloped off.

In the woods near Herndon, Virginia, seven Union pickets had joined together around a campfire to keep warm. They were playing cards, joking and talking softly to each other as they played. Every now and then, one picket walked away to listen. Everything seemed quiet and peaceful. Not even a twig cracked in the clear, cold January night.

Toward midnight, a sound suddenly broke the stillness — the sound of a pistol shot.

Before the men could spring to their feet or reach for their guns, each man was grabbed from behind and felt his arms being pinned to his sides. Almost without a sound, the prisoners were herded together, their guns and sabers taken from them. Without a sound, seven horses were bridled and saddled and, along with the prisoners, were led away. It took only five minutes. Not even a playing card remained at the end of that time. There was only the flickering flame of the campfire, lighting the dark woods.

Through the trees, quietly, silently, went Mosby, his nine men, his seven captives and their seven horses. After about two miles, they came to a rail fence and in the distance another campfire could be seen. Mosby spoke in a sharp whisper.

"Drop to the ground," he ordered the captives.

"Guard them," he ordered one of his men.

Then off he went with the rest of his squad. Soon they were back, bringing five more prisoners and leading five more horses. With the twelve men and twelve horses, the squad headed toward Confederate Headquarters.

By the time Mosby's squad reached Fredericksburg, they had captured twice their number of prisoners and more than twice their number of horses.

Jeb Stuart was jubilant. "Your plan is working, John," he told Mosby with a hearty laugh and a slap on the back. "You can have fifteen of my men. Bring us more horses."

Within weeks, Mosby and his band had the Federal lines terrorized. Raid after raid took place right under the shadow of the capitol, always within enemy lines.

They were a strange band. The first group that were loaned to him from the cavalry was called back to its unit. From then on the men that rallied around Mosby were stranger than those in the band of Robin

Mosby's riders

Hood. Never more than three hundred and fifty at the most, and usually just a handful, Mosby's riders would gather at his call; ragged, rough heroes ready to fight at all hours of the day or night.

A white-haired woodsman, John Underwood by name, was one of Mosby's best men. He knew every hidden cave, every hidden path in the mountains and forests of Mosby's Confederacy — as the strip of land came to be known where the squad did its fighting.

There was Hibbs, a gray-haired blacksmith, his old felt hat riddled with holes, and his army coat held together with one Confederate button. By his side rode Chapman, a preacher who chanted Bible verses as he galloped. An Englishman amongst them wore his British uniform and carried a British sword. A sailor, Big Yankee Ames, who had once served in the navy and had run away from the Yankee cavalry, became one of Mosby's most trusted men.

Out of nowhere the men poured; old men and boys, all eager to follow this brave new leader. Wounded soldiers, some in bandages, some on crutches, sneaked out of hospitals to fight at night and sneaked back in the morning to rest and get well.

"These men of Mosby's are not soldiers," sputtered Percy Wyndham, one of the Union cavalry colonels. "They are nothing but horse thieves."

Mosby grinned when he heard this, but he did not like his men called horse thieves. He sent back word to Colonel Wyndham, "Every horse that we stole had a rider and every rider had a carbine, saber and pistol." He vowed to himself that he would capture Wyndham one day and make him take back those words.

Mosby knew that his men were part of the Confederate Army, formed for the purpose of helping to confuse and harass the enemy. "We are regular troops who wear the uniform at all times, only we break up and hide after each fight," said Mosby. Later, by order of Robert E. Lee, they became known as the 43rd Virginia Battalion of Cavalry, although they were often spoken of as Mosby's Rangers, or Mosby's Raiders, or Mosby's Men.

As for Mosby himself, from the day he formed his band, he became a hunted man. He was one of the last men to return home when the Civil War was over. During the rest of his service in the Confederate Army he never knew a moment in which danger was not waiting for him, night and day.

★ 8 ★

Kidnapping of a General

DRIZZLING rain mixed with melting snow was falling. It was 2 A.M. and cold. In the dense black pine woods, twenty-nine of Mosby's men on horses moved through the curtain of darkness, feeling their way among the trees. Oilcloth coats covered their gray uniforms. At the end of the woods, as they neared the village of Fairfax, they dismounted and gathered around their leader. He sat his horse like a black statue — the curling plume on his hat wet and dripping in the night. Each man was alert, but perfectly quiet, hand on his horse, ready to stifle the slightest neigh or whinny. All ears were tuned to catch the sharp, low, almost whispered orders that Mosby was giving.

Not one of the men except Big Yankee Ames, who had guided them, realized how deep they were inside enemy lines and how dangerous was their position. No man could have passed through that woods or along those roads by daylight without being instantly recognized and captured by Union soldiers.

Just ahead of them lay the village of Fairfax, headquarters of the Union officers. Three miles to the right, at Centerville, several thousand Yankee troops were massed. The railroad to Fairfax was heavily guarded. Outposts encircled the town. And in the village several hundred of Wyndham's cavalry lay sleeping, confident that no human being would be about on a night such as this.

"Work fast!" Mosby ordered, in his sharp low voice. "In our raincoats we may pass for Yankee cavalry. Divide into squads and scatter. Ames, you and your men go on ahead to capture the patrols and sentinels. Underwood, take your squad to the stables in the village. Hibbs, proceed to the quarters of the officers – the town is full of them. Jo, ride on to the railroad station and see that the telegraph wires are cut so that no messages can go out."

He paused for a moment. "Hunter – you and I will take care of Colonel Wyndham," he said, his eyes flashing eagerly.

"We will meet in the square at the Courthouse in one hour. No firing unless necessary."

With a click of revolvers and a swish of oilcloth

coats, the men mounted their horses and set off on a quick trot toward the quiet village. In the darkness, not one of the sleepy patrols — until he felt the cold steel of a revolver at his head — realized that the men were unfriendly troops.

A disappointment was in store for Mosby. Colonel Wyndham had left that very afternoon for Washington. However, one of the captured guards let fall a bit of news. A general — General Stoughton — lay sleeping in Fairfax that night.

House in Fairfax, Va., where Colonel Mosby captured General Stoughton

Mosby's eyes flashed with delight.

A general! Far better than a colonel! What a break! What a prize!

Taking Hunter and several men with him, Mosby galloped to the door of the general's quarters.

Leaving three men as guards and in charge of the horses, he knocked boldly on the door.

A window opened above.

"Who's there?" asked a sleepy voice.

"The 5th New York Cavalry – an important message for General Stoughton," answered Mosby.

In a few moments footsteps could be heard coming down the stairs. A light flickered in the open doorway as an aide in a nightshirt opened it.

"Take me to the general's bedroom," commanded Mosby.

As the man hesitated, Mosby stepped up, jammed his pistol into the fellow's ribs and whispered his name in the man's ear. White and shaking, the aide led the way to the bedroom and struck a light. On the bed lay General Stoughton, snoring, his body hunched under the covers.

Throwing back the bed clothes and pulling up the general's nightshirt, Mosby gave him a whack on his behind.

"Wake up," he commanded, his blue eyes hard as ice.

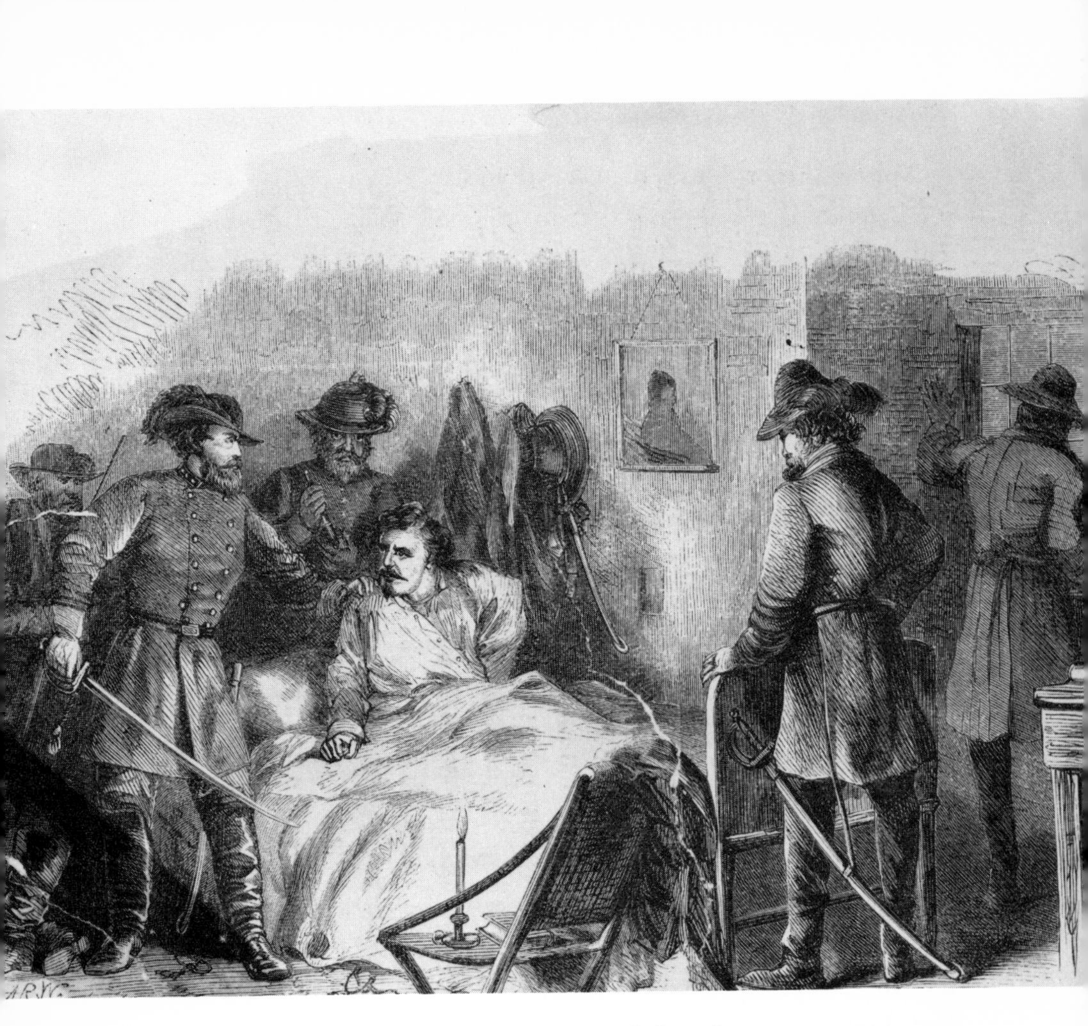

Capture of General Stoughton

Sputtering and angry and still half asleep the general sat up.

"What's the meaning of this?" he demanded angrily.

"Did you ever hear of Mosby?"

"Certainly," answered the general. "What about it? Is he captured?"

"He has just captured you. Get up and dress. Be quick."

The little captain waited impatiently while Stoughton stood in front of a looking glass, dressing with shaking fingers. "You are not getting ready for a dress parade, Stoughton," he said sharply.

Then down the stairs came the general and his aide, closely guarded by Mosby and Hunter. Horses were outside. They mounted and rode off to the meeting place in the courtyard.

What a sight met their eyes! Each squad of men stood waiting, with prisoners – many of them officers – and horses. Each squad had captured three times its number in prisoners. More than a hundred men and horses waited in silence in the deserted street. There was no sound from the sleeping village – not a shot had been fired that night. Had one volley sounded, a thousand men could have come to the rescue of the northern general.

The line fell into order behind Mosby. He handed the reins of Stoughton's horse to Hunter.

"Guard him with your life," he commanded sharply.

Slowly they moved out toward the pike, huddled deep in their saddles. Danger surrounded them on all sides.

On the pike they halted and listened. Only the muted call of an owl could be heard from the woods. But dawn was coming. The sky was growing lighter. The rain had stopped. They must hurry.

On they went until the fort at Centerville came into view through the mist. Cannons bristled in the faint light. Sentinels walked on duty.

Mosby paused briefly. He gave his men a quick, low command, then raised his hand.

Following his lead, putting spurs to their tired horses, they trotted forward down the pike, pounding hoofs drumming on the hard road.

Past the white tents of the fort, filled with sleeping soldiers, they rode.

Past the sentinel who called, "Who goes there?" and then lifted his hand in salute as they galloped by past the heavy frowning guns. They were through the Union lines at last!

But a new danger faced them. Cub Run was a small stream which Mosby had planned to cross to reach Confederate territory. But that morning Cub Run was a swift river, swollen with melting snow and rain into a torrent of water.

There was no turning back — no other road to choose and not a moment to lose.

Mosby plunged into the torrent, Stoughton and Hunter by his side. The men followed and the horses fought the current and swam to the other shore.

As they reached the bank, the sun rose. Mosby felt his heart lift like a bird soaring to the skies. They were safe. Not a man nor a horse was lost. This was a deed that had never been done before in the history of war. Stuart and General Lee would be pleased.

Stuart was overjoyed, and his hearty laughter boomed out when he heard of the kidnapping of General Stoughton. "The gallant band of Captain Mosby shares his glory as they did the danger," he said warmly.

General Lee, having already made Mosby a captain, said, "I wish I could receive his appointment as major that I might announce it to him."

President Abraham Lincoln said, "I do not mind losing a Union general. I can make another general in five minutes. But I hate to lose the horses!"

Only two months had passed since Mosby had formed his strange little band. Already he was a captain and a hero.

★ 9 ★

The Trap

"COUNT your horses, the Yankees are coming!"

The sudden shrill cry shattered the early morning quiet which lay over a deserted old farm near Leesburg, Virginia.

In the huge barn of the farm, sixty-five of Mosby's exhausted men lay sleeping in the hay. Their horses, unsaddled, unbridled, were in the barnyard, tied to the high board fence which surrounded the house and barn. Mosby and several others lay stretched on blankets in front of the hearth inside the farmhouse.

Through a narrow gate in a fence around the farm which bordered on the pike, a horseman came galloping madly. As the sun rose in the dawn of the morning, he galloped across the field and through a second wider gate which opened into the barnyard. The gate banged shut behind him, and he shouted again,

"The Yankees are coming!
The Yankees are coming!"

The sound of galloping hoofbeats, the sharp crash of the gate, the cry of the sentry, brought Mosby to his feet. Snatching up his pistols, he belted them on and rushed out the door into the barnyard.

"Saddle – mount –" he screamed to the men who came tumbling half asleep, out of house and barn. "Mount, but do not fire!"

A horde of blue figures – two hundred of them – were streaming through the pike gate and across the field. On toward the farm buildings galloped the wave of blue, firing rifles and carbines against the fence and house and barn as they came. As they neared the fence they scattered, drawing their sabers. They surrounded the house and blocked the barnyard and the sixty-five men who were trapped inside.

Leaping onto their horses, at Mosby's command, Mosby's men surged forward. Bridle reins in teeth, revolvers in hands, their eyes were on their leader.

Mosby, still on foot, ran between the horses' heads and kicked open the wide barnyard gate.

"Charge," he screamed, in a piercing voice. For a moment it seemed as if he would be crushed as the

Charging surprised Yankees

men poured toward the opening. One man jumped down, threw the reins of his horse to Mosby and ran on on foot.

"Charge 'em, go through 'em," screamed Mosby again, his eyes blazing. Leaping on to the horse and pushing forward to lead the fighting, he galloped out into the field with the speed of an arrow.

Yelling like madmen, Mosby's men poured out behind him, charging right into the surprised Yankees who thought they had their enemy cornered, trapped and captured. With revolvers smoking, standing up in their stirrups, the men in gray met the sabers of the men in blue. With almost every pistol shot, a Yankee saddle was emptied and a heavy body fell, before a saber could strike. Mosby was everywhere, his piercing yell ringing out, both pistols smoking.

Mosby's men were outnumbered three to one. Yet the furious fire, the unexpected charge, the yells of the men, turned the Yankee charge into a terrified panic. Back, back, the attacking raiders pushed the men in blue. When their captain was shot down, the Yankees gave way. A struggle began to get back to the pike gate. Some galloping, some running on foot, they tried to force themselves and their horses through.

But the gate was too narrow. Struggling and screaming, the Yankees jammed up there. Their horses reared and plunged and screamed as Mosby's men poured a death fire into the backs of the desperate Union soldiers.

Some of the riders broke through the fence and rushed away down the pike, with Mosby at their heels. By the time he returned, the farm field was so filled with dead and wounded that a flag of truce had been raised. A hospital was set up right there on the field. As Mosby galloped through, a young Union lieutenant, very seriously wounded, beckoned to him.

"Give me some of my own men to nurse me," he begged. "I'm dying."

Mosby looked at the young boy, pityingly. He allowed him to choose two of the eighty-two captured prisoners to stay beside him. He detailed other prisoners as a burial squad and Confederates and Federals together took care of the wounded and helped to bury the dead.

Mosby's loss was four men injured.

Taken entirely by surprise, trapped as perfectly as any enemy would have wished, with only one exit, not a man mounted and most of them asleep, Mosby had accomplished another miracle!

A letter dated "Headquarters, April 4, 1863," said, "I have the pleasure to send by return courier to Major Mosby his commission of Major."

The letter was signed, "Robert E. Lee."

This was just two weeks after the capture of General Stoughton. Mosby had been a captain then. Now he was a major. It happened on the first day of April — April Fool's Day, 1863.

★ 10 ★

Burning of a Train

IT was spring, the spring of 1863. May filled the marshy woodlands with flowering white dogwood, bluebells, and green jack-in-the-pulpits, and filled the roads ankle-deep with mud.

General Lee had begun to move his armies north toward Washington. No one knew just when Mosby — the little major so greatly feared by the northern soldiers — might take it into his head to mount the steps of the capitol. He had threatened to do just that — had sent a lock of his hair to President Lincoln and a message. "I'll be up to see you soon." President Lincoln had laughed.

Nevertheless, the bridges around Washington, over the Potomac River, Chain Bridge, Long Bridge, and the Aqueduct were being heavily guarded and the boards of their floors taken up each night. Six thousand northern soldiers, one whole division, was held there to protect the city against Mosby.

General Stuart had sent Mosby a small howitzer, a tiny cannon, with a suggestion that he try his hand at destroying the railways that carried troops in and out of Washington.

Rail lines were very heavily guarded also. There were camps of soldiers every two miles, pickets riding back and forth, and on each train were armed troops. Through this heavily guarded line, Mosby must attack.

"If you can stop supplies from reaching the Union troops, either on the roads or by rail, you will break the heart line of the enemy," Stuart wrote.

"This would be worth losing everything for – the gun – even our lives. How many will join me on it?" Mosby wondered.

That evening, although it was spring, red flannel underwear hung on the clotheslines of some of the homes around Warrenton. Children skipped from door to door. Mosby was operating his "grapevine."

Forty men answered his call. Chapman, the preacher, was given three men and put in charge of the howitzer. He started off, chanting a Bible verse in a loud, clear voice. "He shall cover thee with his feathers and under his wings shalt thou trust."

Destroying the railroad in Grant's rear

Into the dark pine woods the men rode, as close to the railroad as they dared. They hid themselves and their horses and lay down to sleep on the ground around their gun. The enemy's camp was so close that they were awakened by the enemy bugles sounding reveille.

Quickly and silently each man went about his appointed work. Telegraph wires were cut. The railroad ties were pried loose and turned toward the bank.

The howitzer was covered with pine branches and placed with great care where it could send its shells hurtling straight into the train.

One man was to wait at the turn of the road and to give a signal when the train approached. The rest stayed in hiding, lying flat on the ground, listening to the buzz of insects in the underbrush, fingers on their revolvers.

Time passed.

A northern picket walked by. He did not see the eyes in the thickets, nor the gleam of the gun under the pine branches.

Finally, after a long wait, the guard waved his arms, swinging them about in big circles, then ducked and ran.

At last the train was coming. The men in hiding

could hear a panting, rumbling sound. They could see the trail of smoke far off. They could see the engineer leaning out, watching the tracks to see that roads were clear. The train chugged along until suddenly, with a screeching of metal on rails, it began to slide to one side and the engine and twelve cars slipped into a soft mud bank.

Immediately, there was a loud roar from the howitzer. A shell exploded and flew into the cars. Another terrific roar and a shell hit the boiler. Hot steam rushed out.

Mosby's men leaped to their feet and with blood curdling Rebel yells, they appeared on all sides, their revolvers smoking and blazing fire. The Yankee troops were blocked inside the train.

In a panic they fought to escape, anywhere, out of the train into the woods, away from Mosby. As the Yankees stampeded, Mosby's men ransacked the train, seizing mailbags, supplies, food and medicines.

Mosby did not stop to capture prisoners. Through the noise of firing, he heard the bugle of the northern cavalry and the roll of their drums. They too had heard the bellow of the howitzer and were on their way toward the railroad.

"Set fire to the cars. Then scatter," Mosby ordered. "Carry only what you can pack or hide in the woods. We will try to save the howitzer. Six of us will guard the rear. Chapman, three of you go ahead with the gun."

As the men rode off into the woods, the railroad train burst into flames.

A dozen Yankee horsemen came into view, riding swiftly. Hundreds more were on the way.

As they reached the woods, Mosby and the six men of the rear guard whirled and charged. Revolvers cracked. Sabers flashed in the hand-to-hand fighting. The underbrush echoed with shouts and crashing horses' hoofs.

"We're outnumbered. Retreat," Mosby ordered. They turned and galloped off into a narrow lane between two fences. The lane led up a hill. Chapman and his men stopped at the top of the little hill. He turned his cannon about, faced it toward the enemy and reloaded it. Mosby's six men joined the others beside the cannon. They waited tense and silent, guns cocked.

Up the hill, through the lane, rode the boys in blue, four abreast. With only fifty yards to go, Mosby barked an order.

"Fire!"

A shell hurtled downward, into the men and animals of the Union ranks.

Men dropped from the saddles of their rearing

horses. The horses screamed and plunged and backed into one another.

Quickly Chapman reloaded.

As the brave northern horsemen again surged forward the cannon belched.

"Charge," yelled Mosby. Shouting and screaming his men charged down the hill, their pistols cracking death.

But as the front lines fell, more and more cavalrymen poured in from the rear.

Again Mosby retreated.

Again the cannon roared.

Again he and his men charged.

But this time the northern soldiers came straight through Mosby's fire. In the hand-to-hand fighting around the gun, Mosby saw that they were hopelessly surrounded. Chapman was wounded. Hoskins was killed.

"Every man for himself!" shouted Mosby.

Still fighting, both pistols raining fire against the enemy sabers he put spurs to his horse and shot straight down the hill through the Union lines. As he rode into the woods, his head low on his horse's neck, the jubilant cheers of the Yankees rang in his ears. The gun which had been so gallantly defended had been captured.

It had cost a heavy price.

Mosby had lost one of his most trusted men. Many Union soldiers had been wounded or killed.

Yet Jeb Stuart had nothing but praise for Mosby when he heard the news of the train raid and the capture of the gun.

"You have cracked the supply line. Continue this work. Capture trains and wagons — rail or horse drawn — take their stores, their food, their ammunition, their horses and their men. I will send you another cannon."

★ 11 ★

Mosby Retaliates

THE northern general, Little Phil Sheridan, was furious at John Mosby for destroying his supply lines. For the entire year of 1864 Mosby had stuck close to his "Confederacy," just over the mountains from Sheridan, blocking and harassing the Union troops, protecting and guarding Virginia. Sheridan decided to try to burn Mosby out.

He set fire to the beautiful Shenandoah Valley; its farms, its homes, its fields of corn and wheat. He turned it into a desert, a land of ruin, its fences burned, its roads mud holes, its fields patches of weeds. A price was put on Mosby's head. The Union offered an unlimited sum to any man who would find and kill him. "Hunt him with squads, regiments, brigades," Sheridan ordered. "But get him. And hang him on the spot."

When President Lincoln freed the slaves in 1862, the North hoped the men of the South would stop fighting, go home and plant crops. Now two years later they asked, "Why doesn't the South give up?" For the men and their families were facing a winter of terrible hardship with no food and no homes. The soldiers were ragged and dirty, many without shoes. Often they went for days with nothing to eat but hard tack and slices of salt pork or a handful of parched corn. The Union Army on the other hand was becoming stronger and tougher. It was constantly supplied with new men and new stores.

Mosby wore the two stars of a lieutenant colonel now. But he was not as gay and jaunty as he had been. His eyes were as keen and flashing, his endurance as great. But his mouth had tightened, his voice had sharpened and his manner was one of fierce command. Like General Lee, Mosby was feeling the strain of war. Both Grumble Jones, his first captain, and his loved friend and admired commander, Jeb Stuart, had been killed in battle. The death of the daring cavalry general was a great loss to the South.

Mosby was deeply hurt and never quite got over his sense of personal loss. He was directly under the command of Robert E. Lee now and took his orders from him. Lee was growing old. He had suffered serious defeats; first at Gettysburg, then throughout the whole South. Ulysees S. Grant, "Unconditional Surrender Grant," was in command of all the Union armies. He had followed Lee and pressed him hard and had pushed him back, back, toward Richmond. Lee's armies were wearing out — the gray line was becoming thin. The Confederate Government had lost everything but the states of Virginia and North and South Carolina.

"Aside from my army at Richmond, yours is the only force to protect Virginia," Lee wrote Mosby.

Mosby did not fail Lee. To get needed supplies and livestock for the Confederate Army, he kept his men

The Rebels retreating with their plunder across the river.

in their saddles until they could ride their mounts sleeping. All during that summer of 1864 he sent Lee reports of his raids.

Aug. 4 – Captured 30 wagons, 70 horses and mules. 10 men were with me.

Aug. 11 – captured 19 wagons, valuable stores, saddles, bridles, horses.

Aug. 24 – Over 100 horses, 12 prisoners, arms, etc. We burned bridges. My loss was 2 men.

Sometimes Mosby used a full company of men on his raids. Sometimes he would divide his men and would hit three or four widely separated outposts in one night. He and his men used every trick at their command to capture wagon trains and supply wagons. They dressed as teamsters and climbed on the seats of the wagon trains, drove them away and looted them. They hung cowbells around the necks of their horses to cover the approach and sound of the horses' hoofs. They backed horses down the road so that it looked as though they had ridden on ahead.

At Berryville, one of his most successful raids, Mosby captured an enormous Yankee wagon train on its way to Sheridan's army. Seventy-five wagons went up in flames. He captured two hundred beef cattle, two hundred prisoners, six hundred mules, and other supplies. His men, three hundred of them, rode away from Berryville on a triumphant twenty-five mile

Mosby and his men capturing the wagon trains.

parade, leading their strings of horses and mules, wearing fancy hats and coats and sashes over their uniforms, playing on fiddles and horns they had salvaged. Blankets and gay quilts hung over the horses' backs; bags of sugar and coffee were strapped to the sides, and packages of all sorts were fastened to the saddles. All these supplies went to the starving armies at Richmond.

"We must keep Lee's army fed," Mosby said.

Mosby was wounded several times in these raids on supplies. But he never let the fighting stop even for a day. When he had to leave his command, one of his men was put in charge.

One morning the men returned from a raid bringing Yankee prisoners with them. Captain Richards was in charge. As they passed through the town of Front Royal, they saw a sight that stopped them in their tracks. Hanging by the neck from a walnut tree on a hill, were two of Mosby's men. On one uniform was a note: "This will be the fate of Mosby and all his men."

Furious, the soldiers rode back into Front Royal. They found that not two but six of Mosby's men had been executed without trial. The soldiers demanded of Captain Richards that six Yankee prisoners be hanged in their places. But Captain Richards refused.

"Colonel Mosby must decide this," he said.

When Mosby was able to return to his men, he began to search for the one who had been responsible for the executions. A northern general, General Custer, had marched the men to their deaths. Four of them were shot, hands tied behind their backs, while a Yankee band was playing.

A seventeen-year-old boy who had joined Mosby's ranks only the day before, and had never yet been in a fight, was one of those who had been led to death. Sobbing and crying, he was tied and dragged behind a Union horseman.

Mosby was cold with anger. "This brutality must stop," he decided. "We will retaliate. But only with men from Custer's command. The men we have already captured are prisoners of war and should be shown courtesy."

A month later, twenty-seven of Custer's men were brought to Mosby, heavily guarded. Among the prisoners was a boy as young as the one from Mosby's squad – a drummer boy, too young to fight.

"Measure for measure," murmured Mosby, looking at the boy sadly.

Then he turned to the Union prisoners.

"There are twenty-seven men here. Let them line up and draw lots. Six men must die."

A hat was brought in with the ballots shaken about in it. In single file, the prisoners marched up and

The captives drawing lots

drew. The drummer boy's face turned white as he looked at his paper and he stood up very straight. An officer cried out in great relief, "Thank God" when he found his slip was blank.

Mosby looked at the men who were to die. He looked at the boy. His grim face softened.

"Come here," he ordered. Then to the rest of the men, "Pass the hat again. There is one marked ballot left to be drawn." And he put the boy's ballot back in the hat.

Slowly the men handed the hat down the line. The officer who had cried out drew the marked paper. He must take the place of the boy.

Under heavy guard, the six men were marched down the highway toward Sheridan's headquarters. Mosby's men looked grim and sober and unhappy. This was the sort of task they hated.

When the officer who had nearly escaped death before suddenly galloped off, a shot was fired after him but no one chased him. Later another prisoner tried the same trick. His horse slipped and fell but no one even turned to see what happened to him.

Late that afternoon when General Custer came riding along the high road, he found three of his men hanging there.

On the coat of one man a note said, "Measure for measure."

That night Mosby wrote a letter to General Sheridan. He told him of the hangings of his own men and the note found, then of Custer's men and the note which he had left. He told Sheridan that seven hundred prisoners had been brought in by Mosby's men but that only three had been hanged — three of Custer's command. And he also said that in the future, any prisoner falling into his hands would be treated with kindness unless some new act of cruelty on the part of the northern armies compelled him to act differently.

Mosby found no more hangings after that.

Years later, many years after the war was over, Mosby received a walking stick with a silver head. On the head of the stick were these words:

> TO COL. JOHN S. MOSBY
> FROM THE DRUMMER BOY

★ 12 ★

Greenbacks

THE lonely whistle of a locomotive echoed through the Virginia hills about 2 A.M. on a cold October morning.

In one of the cars of the Baltimore and Ohio railroad train which puffed along the tracks four Union officers sat huddled around a little coal stove. The oil lanterns, swinging from the ceiling of the car, cast strange shadows over the men's faces. One of the officers was a major. He held out his hands to the comforting warmth, but his feet he kept firmly propped on a metal box on the floor.

"Is the train very crowded?" one of the officers asked the conductor as he came through the car, swinging another lantern.

"Only a few businessmen, some women who are

asleep, and a group of immigrants who cannot speak a word of English. They must have just come from Ellis Island, probably don't even know we are at war. They are heading west to their relatives."

"Let's hope the tiger Mosby is not on the prowl tonight," said one of the men fearfully, looking out the window into the darkness.

The conductor rested his lantern on the dusty arm of a seat.

"If Mosby's men board this train," he said, "it is you gentlemen who must look to yourselves. He will take you and all you have. But he will not touch the rest of the passengers. He has never been known to harm a civilian."

The major shifted his feet uneasily on his box as the conductor picked up his lantern and left the car.

The train puffed along noisily for some time. It came to a narrow passageway between two hills. Suddenly, there was a screech of wheels. The engine sputtered — the cars swerved on their tracks. They leaned crazily, then rolled slowly to a stop, leaning their sides against the steep banks. Quickly the major snatched his blue cape from his shoulders and covered the metal box.

A wild Rebel yell filled the morning air, as eighty men in gray uniforms leaped on to the train and started through the cars.

Three of Mosby's men entered the car where the officers were. As one of the Union officers raised his gun to fire, a shot rang out and the Union man dropped to the floor.

"Step outside," said one of the Mosby men. "Come on. We don't want to hurt you. Colonel Mosby is waiting."

The major sat still. The Ranger gave him a shove and as he did so, the cape slipped from the box.

Instantly another of Mosby's men picked it up. "Hm – heavy," he said. He shoved his gun into the major's ribs. "On your way," he ordered.

The women who had been sleeping awoke. Two young girls looked up in terror as two Confederates entered their car, guns in hand. "We are frightened, Sirs," one of them cried pleadingly.

One of the soldiers swept off his hat and made a bow. "I'll protect you," he said. "There is no need for you to go into the cold yet." And as the other soldier herded the rest of the women through the train, he sat down between the two girls.

In the car where the immigrants sat, not one of them moved. They sat with their bundles of luggage piled around them, waiting patiently for the train to move on. The women had scarves tied about their heads. The men were dressed in strange foreign clothes. None of them spoke.

Several Confederates burst into the door. "Come on, out you go," cried one of them, waving his gun.

No one moved.

"They don't understand us," cried one of the soldiers. He took off his hat and bowed, pointing to the door. "This way, this way," he shouted.

The immigrants settled back in their seats.

Just then one soldier stumbled over a pile of newspapers lying near the stove.

"Ah, these will talk," he cried. "Give me a match." As the papers flared up on the floor, the men and women grabbed up their bundles and rushed for the door.

As the last of the people left the cars, flames began to crackle through the train and soon it was ablaze.

One figure stood on the bank above the train. Colonel Mosby had not taken an active part in this raid. He was still a cripple from his last raid. One leg was bandaged where a horse had stepped on it and had broken his foot. He leaned heavily on a cane.

"The passengers are free to go at will," he directed. "They must take care of themselves." Then he turned to his men.

"Get the prisoners together," he ordered. "They will ride with us. Two of you take this box and ride on to the mountains at once. Guard it well. I think it is what we are looking for."

The greenback raid

Just then one of the prisoners was led up to Mosby. Wearing no coat but a white linen blouse, he was shivering with cold. He was a strange-looking figure in heavily embroidered trousers and shining boots. His teeth chattered beneath his little waxed mustache.

"This is an officer from Austria," explained the smiling Confederate who held him by the arm. "He wants to join the Union army. He is angry because some one just robbed him of his coat. He wants it back."

"Why did you come across the ocean to fight against the South," asked Mosby.

"To learn war, to learn lessons in the tac'-tics of war," faltered the Austrian in broken English.

"Losing your coat is your first lesson in tactics," laughed Mosby.

As the Austrian turned away, the soldier who was guarding him said, "Say, those fancy breeches of yours have a better seat in them than mine. Besides you won't need them in prison where you are going. And my boots are clean wore-out. Come on — how about a trade?"

And so in the cold gray light of the morning, the trade was made and the Austrian walked dejectedly away in torn gray pants and worn-out boots. The soldier shouted after him, "Your second lesson in tactics, sir." Then he took several waltz steps in his fancy new embroidered trousers.

After the prisoners had been delivered to headquarters, Mosby and his men joined the two who had gone ahead over the mountains with the box.

When they opened it, they found a treasure! One hundred and sixty-eight thousand dollars in greenbacks – pay which was to have been given to Sheridan's Union armies.

What a find!

Army law allows the spoils to go to the victors. One hundred sixty-eight thousand dollars ($168,000) to divide between eighty men!

"It is yours, men," Mosby said. "You have taken it fairly." Twenty-one hundred dollars went to each man who had ridden with him that night. Mosby himself did not take a penny. Never, in any raid, did he take anything captured from the northern armies for himself. It was always divided evenly among his men.

"With these Yankee greenbacks," he said, as he handed each man his share, "buy yourselves the warm uniforms that you badly need. Pay the farmers of the Shenandoah for the food they have so generously given you. Get yourselves the finest horses you can buy. We must be able to protect the South, so that she may never need bow her head to Yankee rule."

★ 13 ★

Narrow Escapes

"THE only fault I have to find with you, Colonel," said General Lee to Mosby, "is that you are always getting wounded."

Nothing would have pleased the enemy more than to capture Mosby, and after a reward had been offered for him, he was hunted even more diligently. Although he was wounded many times, he was always able to get away. Yet several times he had been wounded so seriously he had to be away from his command for several months.

His wife and family had been brought to a home of friends near Middleburg, where Mosby could slip away and see them occasionally. The house was searched often by Union soldiers in the hopes of capturing him on one of these visits. One night, they almost did. The entire household was asleep when there came the sound of horses' hoofs up the quiet country road. His wife, Pauline, awakened first, and clutching Mosby, she shook him awake. Downstairs there was a thunderous knocking on the front door as the Union cavalrymen demanded a search of the house.

"Open up," shouted a hoarse voice.

Instantly Mosby sprang to the window of the bedroom at the rear of the house. The window was open and the limb of a huge walnut tree, heavy with foliage, brushed the outside sill. Grasping the limb, he swung himself across into the tree, crouching close to the trunk in the darkness.

Pauline quickly pulled the blinds and closed the window. She gathered up his colonel's uniform from the chair and stuffed it under some blankets in a chest. She pulled a robe about her, lighted a lamp and walked to the top of the stairs.

As slowly as he dared, Mosby's good friend and host went down the stairs to open the door. He wanted to give Mosby time to conceal himself.

"Here is an extra light," Pauline said, as the soldiers stormed up the stairs. They looked suspiciously at her white face. They pulled at the warm, tumbled covers of the bed. Then into all the rooms they poured. Cupboards and closets were searched. They talked and moved noisily, rapping the bedroom walls with their pistol butts. Back down they went and out into the garden, spearing the boxwood bushes with their sabers, looking into the stables and barns.

"This looks like Mosby's horse, Lady," declared one soldier in great excitement.

"You're crazy, man," scoffed another. "Mosby couldn't disappear without taking his horse. Unless he's a ghost! Sometimes I think that's what he is!"

Finally they rode away, taking all the horses with them, including Lady. Mosby climbed back into the bedroom and laughingly comforted his frightened wife.

"A narrow escape but I made it," he said.

Toward Christmas, Mosby and one of his men, Tom, were on a scouting trip. Enemy troops had been reported near. Mosby had left a wedding party to find out if this was true. He wore a fine new uniform and cape and brand new boots. As it grew dark a drizzle of rain fell which quickly turned to ice. The horses' feet slipped on the wet icy road.

As they came to a house beside the road, the light in the window seemed warm and friendly.

"I know the man who lives here," Mosby said to Tom. "His name is Lake. If we knock on his door, I think he will invite us in to supper. Maybe he will even give us a good cup of real coffee."

Lakeland – house where Colonel Mosby was wounded

"I'll wait outside," Tom said, "just in case of trouble. I'll watch the horses. The northern cavalry is close, even though they do not know we are near."

"Nonsense," Mosby answered, "you're freezing in this icy rain. There's no danger here – none at all – and I could not enjoy my meal with you outside."

Mosby and Tom tied their horses to the railing. As they did so, the door opened and a fat, jolly-looking man beckoned them in to a warm fire and a table set for dinner. Mosby and Tom did not take the time to remove the pistols from their saddle holsters.

They entered gratefully, and after shaking the ice from his scarlet-lined cloak, Mosby folded it and carefully laid it and his hat on a chair by the fireplace to dry.

Soon Mr. Lake, his two daughters, Sarah and Lan-

Ludwell Lake, owner of Lakeland

donia, and the two Rangers were seated at the table. They ate spareribs and fried apples, and enjoyed a friendly conversation. So relaxed was everyone with the good food and the warm fire that, at first, they did not hear the approach of horsemen. The men stopped outside when they saw the light in the windows and the military saddles on the horses tied to the railing.

Mosby and Tom laid their napkins on the table, and Mr. Lake rose to put another log on the fire. Sarah started for the kitchen to get fresh coffee. As she passed the window she heard voices.

"Yankee soldiers," she gasped, drawing back quickly as a face peered in the window.

Mosby rose so hastily that his chair clattered to the floor. As he did so there was a loud laugh, and a drunken voice shouted.

"By jingo, *candles* on the table! Now ain't that nice? Whoops! Let's shoot out the pretty candles."

A shot rang out from the wavering gun aimed through the window. Straight through the glass the bullet came. It missed the candles and sank deep into Mosby's side.

In great pain, blood gushing from his side, Mosby staggered into a bedroom. The northern soldiers rushed in. They took Tom captive; then, following the trail of blood, they pushed into the bedroom.

Mosby lay face down on the floor in a pool of blood. He had found the strength to stuff his military jacket with its insignia of rank under a wardrobe.

The northern officer turned him over and examined the deep dangerous wound.

"He won't live long."

The officer turned to Mr. Lake.

"Who is he?"

"Never saw either of these men before," said Lake. "Ask him who he is."

"Well, Johnny Reb," said the officer, bending down, "Give us your name."

In a whisper, Mosby spoke. "Johnson, Lieutenant Johnson," he said. Then he fainted.

"Well – Johnson, your share in the war is over. We'll leave you here – no use moving you. But your friend must come with us. And I think we'll just pull off these fine army boots and take them along. You'll never wear them again."

The Lakes, thinking Mosby dead, went back to stand by the fire and plan what to do.

They had not stood there long when Mosby came staggering in, his face ashy-white.

"I must get away," he said. "The Yankees may come back. I need a doctor."

"In this rain and ice, man? Impossible!" cried Mr. Lake.

But Landonia spoke quickly. "Our ox cart, Father. We could wrap him in blankets and hide him in the straw. He must have help."

"We must work fast, then," said Mr. Lake. "Run fetch Dan'el, Landonia."

While Landonia hurried to the Negro's cabin in the back of the house, Mr. Lake hastily began to hitch the oxen to the cart. Sarah washed Mosby's wound and stuffed a clean soft sunbonnet over it as a bandage to stop the flow of blood. She pulled off her own homemade shoes and put them on his feet. She and her father wrapped him in soft quilts and piled hay over him. Then off he and Daniel started toward the mountains, in the freezing sleet, behind the slow plodding beasts.

The northern soldiers rode back to camp. They shook out the cape with the scarlet lining and showed the hat with the plume which they had taken from the chair, and the fine black shiny boots. "We killed the man who wore these — his name was Lieutenant Johnson."

"You fools," roared their comrades, "That hat and cape belong to Mosby! We must go back and get him. We must bring him here, dead or alive."

Back they galloped, the whole company of them. They would bring him back. He could not get away. He was dead. No one could move him on such a night.

When they reached the Lake house, they found the family in front of the fire but no trace of the wounded man.

"Where is he?" they demanded furiously. "Tell us at once. Was he Mosby?"

"We don't know where he is and we never saw him before," answered Mr. Lake, quietly.

"And we wouldn't tell you if we did know," sputtered Sarah.

"Out! Out, all of you, while we search!" ordered the captain. "Maybe a bit of sleet and snow will chill that temper of yours, my girl."

The soldiers stormed noisily through the house and over the grounds and out into Daniel's cabin. Back they came to the shivering Lake family.

"Was that John Mosby? Answer! And how did he get away? Answer," shouted the captain, "or you will see your house turn to ashes."

"Your man is dead," said Mr. Lake. "His comrades carried him away for burial. There is nothing you can do about him now."

"Was it Mosby?" thundered the captain. "Tell us, or we will burn your house down."

"Burn on," said Mr. Lake. "The fire will warm us."

"Burn on, burn on," cried Sarah and Landonia.

Frustrated and angry, the soldiers rode away at

last. All through the Union armies, there was dismay and rejoicing.

"We should have captured him," they said. "This time we should have caught him. But at least Mosby is dead. We need fear him no longer."

The fall of Richmond, Va.

★ 14 ★

The Last Meeting

FOR many weeks, Mosby lay close to death. For three months, the 43rd Battalion of the Virginia Company was without a colonel.

It was the time of greatest trial for the armies of Robert E. Lee also, that winter and spring of 1865. Without shoes on their feet, without meat to eat, uniforms held together by rags and by ropes, they had fought the strong Union Army in snow, in mud, in hail, in sleet, and in the blazing sun. Their beloved General Lee could not continue the fight against the iron-willed general, Ulysses S. Grant, any longer. The ragged line of Confederates was too thin and too weak. The Union armies surrounded them on all sides. There was no longer a Confederate capitol. Richmond had fallen. Union troops had marched into a city of empty streets, windows closed and shuttered, white smoke rising from empty tobacco warehouses.

"I would rather die a thousand deaths than surrender," General Lee told his officers.

But on April 9, 1865, General Lee rode to meet General Grant, the dusty mud-spattered "Butcher" Grant, at Appomattox Courthouse to sign the terms of surrender.

Mosby, in his mountain hideaway, was told of the defeat. His face was grim.

"I can't bring myself to believe that the end has come," he said, placing the back of his hand over his eyes.

He heard the story of the surrender of the troops on April 12, listening intently, missing no detail.

Lee, in his splendid full dress uniform, with shining boots and gleaming sword, rode at the head of his silent, heavy-hearted columns.

"No cheering," Grant warned his men.

The Union regiments waited without a sound until the bugles' notes broke the stillness. Instantly the Union soldiers, regiment by regiment, saluted their countrymen as they passed.

Mosby heard all this and his eyes grew dark with sorrow.

"Grant is no butcher," he cried. "He is a generous man. He did not ask for General Lee's sword. He

Capitulation and surrender of Robert E. Lee and his army at Appomattox to Lt. General U. S. Grant

allowed all the officers to keep their side arms and their horses. He treated the Confederate soldiers as countrymen. Already he is sending them food and aid. I should like to know Grant better. I should like to become his friend."

One of Mosby's men banged his fist on the table and spoke with bitterness.

"Colonel, I don't want to live in conquered territory. Let's go to Mexico or to the Far West. Let's get away from the Yankees."

Mosby stopped him with a look of scorn.

"You heard what General Lee told the men at Appomattox. Go home and help build up the South!"

"Will you surrender us then?" asked the man sullenly. "Will you force us to give up our arms and our horses?"

Mosby's lips tightened in a thin line. His face hardened.

"I will not surrender until my government orders it," he decided. "I have had no official word; no guarantee of fair treatment. I will take twenty men with me and discuss a truce with the northern generals. Then you men may decide for yourselves whether you will take your paroles or not."

As the men rode with him toward the Union Army camp, Mosby looked at them and his heart was heavy. A fine-looking group of young men, mounted on fine horses that they had captured by their own bravery.

"What would be the fate of these young men when they laid aside their arms?" he wondered. They were hated by many northern soldiers. And he himself still had a price upon his head!

He patted the neck of the thoroughbred horse that he rode — a gift from this same loyal group of men — a gift that meant more to him than anything he had ever owned. He thought of those first ragged heroes who had rallied to his call, and a lump came into his throat.

When he reached the house where the northern officers waited, Mosby and a few of his men entered.

Calmly and quietly the men sat around a table and talked.

"You must surrender your command, Colonel Mosby," the northern officer told him.

"I will not surrender unless ordered to do so by General Lee," replied Mosby, his blue eyes cold.

The northern general stood up, anger on his face. "Then the truce is at an end," he said.

Just at that moment, the door was thrown open and one of Mosby's men rushed in.

"Colonel," he shouted. "These Yankee devils are

hiding everywhere. They are here to trap us. Let's fight 'em and capture 'em. They are here to trick us."

Mosby leaped to his feet, eyes blazing.

"My men are at your mercy," he said in a cold sharp voice, his hand on the holster of his revolver. "We came here under a truce. The truce is over. You are forcing us to protect ourselves. Follow me, men."

There was a breathless silence.

Walking swiftly, Mosby and his officers went out of the room.

Had one northern officer clicked a revolver or made a move, Mosby and his men might have fought and died that day.

Quickly, they mounted their horses and galloped away, back to the mountains of "Mosby's Confederacy."

The next day, Mosby sent out his last call.

At Salem, Virginia, about seven miles from the place where he had formed his first command, the Rangers gathered – two hundred of them – on a cold, misty spring day.

They formed ranks and their little Colonel rode out to the front and turned and spoke to them.

"Soldiers," he said, "I have summoned you for the last time . . . Our country is now the spoils of the

Mosby summoning his troops for the last time

conqueror. I disband your organization in preference to surrendering it to our enemies. I am no longer your commander . . . I part from you with a just pride in the fame of your achievements. . .Accept the assurance of my unchanging confidence and regard. Farewell."

Mosby dismounted. He could say nothing more. His heart was full.

HERE, APRIL 21, 1865.
COL. JOHN S. MOSBY
DISBANDED HIS
GALLANT PARTISAN
RANGERS – THE
FORTY – THIRD
BATTALION
VIRGINIA CAVALRY

Tears streamed down the faces of the men as they, too, dismounted and came to shake their colonel's hand.

It was almost a year before Mosby could bring himself to receive his own parole and end his war with the Union. He was one of the last men to be mustered out of the Civil War. The Union had been saved. Mosby took the oath of allegiance and began to bend all his efforts toward helping cement it together. He became a lifelong friend of General Grant. He opened his law office and took up civilian life again, with his wife and family.

Mosby lived to be an old man, but the greatest glory of his life was when he was made commander of the 43rd Virginia Battalion of the Cavalry.

Virginia is proud of her son — whose name in the South stands for such bravery and daring.

During the hundred years that have passed since the War between the States, the name of John Mosby has come to be remembered by both North and South. Not only to his southern countrymen but to the whole reunited nation that has never lost its love of courage, he is one of the Great Confederates.

Bibliography

Partisan Life with Colonel John Mosby
Major John Scott
Harper and Bros. N. Y., 1867
Reminiscences of a Mosby Guerilla
John W. Munson
Moffat Yard & Co. N. Y., 1906
Mosby's Memoirs
Edited by Charles Wells Russell
Little Brown & Co. N. Y., 1917
Ranger Mosby
Virgil Carrington Jones
Chapel Hill, University N. Carolina, 1944
Mosby – Gray Ghost of the Confederacy
Jonathan Daniels
Lippincott & Co. N. Y., 1959

Mosby's War Reminiscences
John Mosby
Pageant Book Co. N. Y., 1958
Mosby and His Men
Marshall Crawford
G. W. Carlton & Co., N. Y., 1867
The Blue and the Gray
Henry Steele Commager
Bobbs Merrill Co., Chicago, 1951
The Civil War
Fletcher Pratt
Garden City Books, N. Y., 1955
Mosby's Rangers
James Joseph Williamson
R. B. Kenyon, N. Y., 1896

Index